ANDREW CARTER

MUSICK'S JUBILEE

for soprano and mezzo-soprano soli
mixed chorus and small orchestra

based on a poem by Andrew Marvell
with other verses by John Dryden and Alfred Tennyson

Music Department
OXFORD UNIVERSITY PRESS
Oxford and New York

Oxford University Press, Walton Street, Oxford OX2 6DP, England
Oxford University Press Inc., 200 Madison Avenue, New York, NY 10016, USA

Oxford is a trade mark of Oxford University Press

© Oxford University Press 1995

CONTENTS

Musick's Jubilee was commissioned (with funds from Yorkshire and Humberside Arts)
by Otley Choral Society to celebrate its fiftieth anniversary season
and first performed on 24 April 1993 in Otley Parish Church
by Otley Choral Society and Ilkley Choral Society,
with the Yorkshire Chamber Ensemble conducted by John Coates.

Orchestration: 2 oboes, bassoon, 2 trumpets, organ, timpani, cymbals, strings.

Duration: 25 minutes

MUSICKS EMPIRE

First was the world as one great Cymbal made,
Where Jarring Windes to infant Nature plaid.
All Musick was a solitary sound,
To hollow Rocks and murm'ring Fountains bound.

Jubal first made the wilder Notes agree;
And Jubal tuned Musicks Jubliee:
He called the Ecchoes from their sullen Cell,
And built the Organs City where they dwell.

Each sought a consort in that lovely place;
And Virgin Trebles wed the manly Base.
From whence the Progeny of numbers new
Into harmonious Colonies withdrew.

Some to the Lute, some to the Viol went,
And others chose the Cornet eloquent.
These practising the Wind, and those the Wire,
To sing mens Triumphs, or in Heavens quire.

Then Musick, the Mosaique of the Air,
Did of all these a solemn noise prepare:
With which she gain'd the Empire of the Ear,
Including all between the Earth and Sphear.

Victorious sounds! yet here your Homage do
Unto a gentler Conqueror than you;
Who though He flies the Musick of his praise,
Would with you Heavens Hallelujahs raise.

Andrew Marvell

from
A SONG FOR ST CECILIA'S DAY, 1687

What passion cannot Music raise and quell?
    When Jubal struck the chorded shell,
His listening brethren stood around,
    And, wondering, on their faces fell
To worship that celestial sound:
Less than a god they thought there could not dwell
    Within the hollow of that shell,
    That spoke so sweetly and so well.
What passion cannot Music raise and quell?

John Dryden

from
SONG OF THE LOTOS-EATERS

There is sweet music here that softer falls
Than petals from blown roses on the grass,
Or night-dews on still waters between walls
Of shadowy granite, in a gleaming pass;
Music that gentlier on the spirit lies,
Than tir'd eyelids upon tir'd eyes;
Music that brings sweet sleep down from the
                blissful skies.

Alfred Tennyson

Musick's Jubilee

A poem by Andrew Marvell
With other verses by
John Dryden and Alfred Tennyson

Music by
ANDREW CARTER

1

Printed in Great Britain

OXFORD UNIVERSITY PRESS, MUSIC DEPARTMENT, WALTON STREET, OXFORD OX2 6DP

2

3

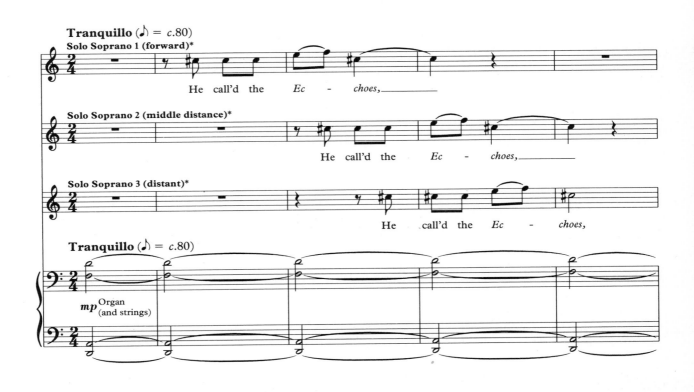

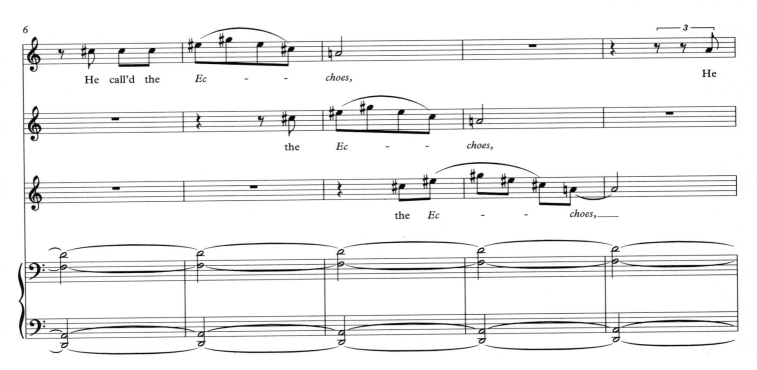

*Ideally out of sight, each singer spaced into the distance.

4

Text by John Dryden *

MEZZO-SOPRANO SOLO

What___ pas - sion___ can - not   Mu - - sic   raise   and   quell?

What___ pas - sion   can-not   Mu - sic   raise and quell?

* From *A Song for St Cecilia's Day*, 1687.

5

6

Text by Alfred Tennyson *

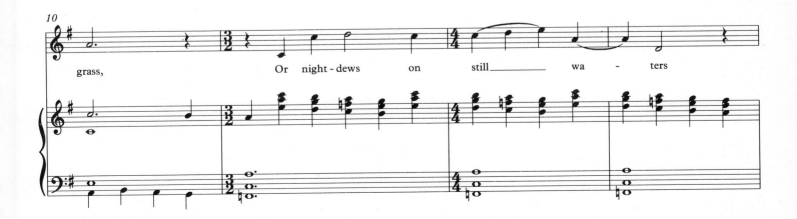

* From *Song of the Lotos Eaters*.

14

be-tween walls_____ Of sha-dowy gra-nite, in a gleam-ing pass;

18

Mu - sic that gent - lier on the

22

spi - rit lies, Than tir - ed* eye - lids up - on ti - red__ eyes;

26

poco rit.

Mu - sic that brings sweet___ sleep

* Modern diphthong – 'ti-ud'.

22

* Modern diphthong – 'ti-ud'.

7

Energico ($\dot{}$ = *c*.80)

attacca No.8

8

Vic - tor - ious sounds!

yet here your Ho - mage do

32

Bishopthorpe, York: Autumn 1992

Music origination Barnes Music Engraving Ltd., East Sussex